Scott Foresman

Good Times We Share

Take a Closer Look

Let's Learn Together

Favorite Things Old and New

Take Me There

Surprise Me!

About the Cover Artist

Maryjane Begin and her family live in Providence, Rhode Island, where she teaches college students when she is not working on her own art. Many of her illustrations—even imaginary places—show how things in Providence look.

ISBN 0-328-01810-4

5 6 7 8 9 10 V063 10 09 08 07 06 05 04 03 02

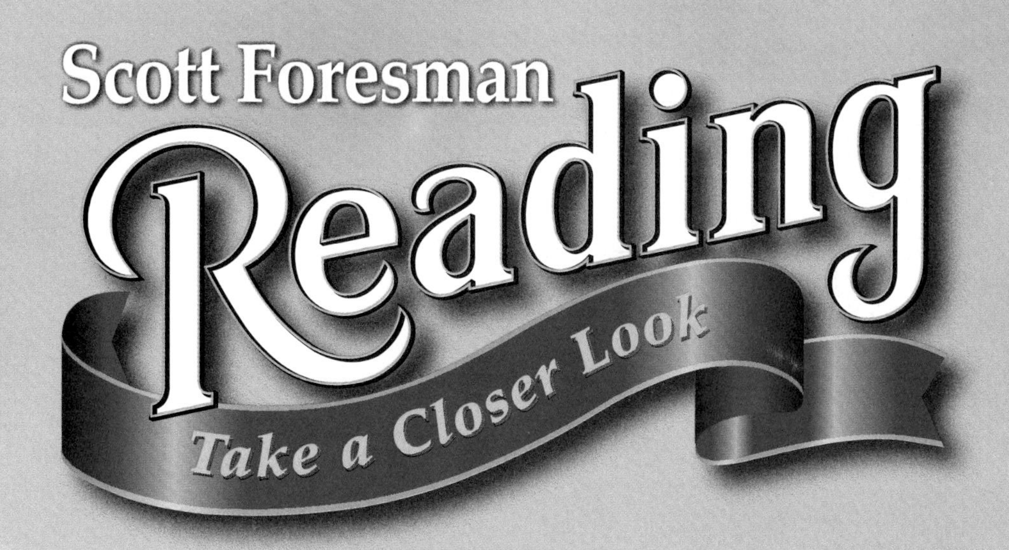

Program Authors

Peter Afflerbach
James Beers
Camille Blachowicz
Candy Dawson Boyd
Wendy Cheyney
Deborah Diffily
Dolores Gaunty-Porter
Connie Juel
Donald Leu
Jeanne Paratore
Sam Sebesta
Karen Kring Wixson

Editorial Offices: Glenview, Illinois • Parsippany, New Jersey • New York, New York
Sales Offices: Parsippany, New Jersey • Duluth, Georgia • Glenview, Illinois
Carrollton, Texas • Ontario, California

Contents

The Nap 10
animal fantasy by Helen Lester
illustrated by Jackie Urbanovic

Oh, Cats! 18
rhyme by Nola Buck
illustrated by Nadine Bernard Westcott

Language Arts Sentences 42

Phonics Story Introduce **Look at That!** 44
realistic fiction by B. G. Hennessy
illustrated by Seth Larson
Science Connection

Apply **Can You Find It?** 52
realistic fiction by Sharon Fear
illustrated by Wendy Edelson
Science Connection

Language Arts Naming Parts 70

Phonics Story Introduce **What Did I See?** 72
realistic fiction by Helen Lester
illustrated by Benton Mahan

Apply **I Went Walking** 80
patterned text by Sue Williams
illustrated by Julie Vivas

Quack, Quack! 111
poem by Dr. Seuss

Language Arts Action Parts 114

Unit 2

Phonics Story Introduce **Fish Mix** 116
photo essay by Judy Nayer
Science Connection

Apply **How Many Fish?** 124
realistic fiction by Caron Lee Cohen
illustrated by S. D. Schindler
Science Connection

One, Two, Three, Four, Five 145
classic poem: a Mother Goose rhyme

Language Arts Word Order. 148

Phonics Story Introduce **Jog, Frog, Jog** 150
animal fantasy by Barbara Gregorich
illustrated by Bernard Adnet

Apply **Tadpole to Frog** 158
expository nonfiction by Fay Robinson
Science Connection

Notice 167
poem by David McCord

Language Arts Telling Sentences 170

Phonics Story Introduce **A Big Job** 172
realistic fiction by Kana Riley
illustrated by Stacey Schuett
Science Connection

Apply **Sweet Potato Pie** 180
rhyme by Anne Rockwell
illustrated by Carolyn Croll

Language Arts Asking Sentences 200

Words I Know 202

Test Talk 204
Taking a Test

Pictionary: Animals 206

Unit 2

Take a Closer Look

Look closely!
Now what can
we see?

The Nap

by Helen Lester

illustrated by Jackie Urbanovic

I am on my mat.

I will have a nap.

Away I go.

Look at that!

Wag, wag, wag.

I like my cap.
Can I have the bat?

Will it go up?
Will it come down?

No. Not on the dad!

No. Not on the cat!

Look at that!

What a nap!

Oh, Cats!

by Nola Buck

illustrated by Nadine Bernard Westcott

I can see cats.
One, two, three cats.

I can say cats.
Come and play, cats.

Up you go, cats.

No, no, no, cats.

Where are you, cats?

I see two cats.

I will come, cats,
to find one cat.

Now I see cats.
One, two, three cats.

You come down, cats.
Come down now, cats.

Jump and play, cats.

Run away, cats?

No, no, no, cats.

Do not go, cats.

If you stay, cats,
we will play, cats.

Up to you, cats.
Be my new cats.

Like you so, cats.

Oh, cats!

About the Illustrator

Nadine Bernard Westcott liked to draw as a child. She did "sketches on the back of restaurant paper place mats."

When she was a child, she dressed her cat in doll's clothes. How would the cats in the story like that? Now she likes to draw cats.

Read Together

Reader Response

Let's Talk

If you were the girl, how would you make the cats stay?

Let's Think

Should you try to make friends with every animal you meet? Why?

Test Prep

Let's Write

The girl in the story talks in rhyme. Now you make rhyming lines.

The girl and the cats
can slip and slide.

The girl and the cats
can __ and __.

Name a Cat

Which cat in the story would you like to have?

1. Make a picture of a new cat who might be in the story.
2. Think of a name for your cat.
3. Write the name under the picture.

Read Together

Language Arts

Sentences

A **sentence** is a group of words that tells a complete idea.

A sentence begins with a capital letter.

Many sentences end with a **.** .

The lion eats**.**

This is a sentence.

It tells what the lion does.

Talk

Look at the pictures.

Tell what a person or animal does.

Write

Write the sentences.

Circle the capital at the beginning.

Circle the period at the end.

1. The shiny seal dives.

2. The clown sells ice cream.

3. The polar bears swim.

Write your own sentences.

Make each tell a complete idea.

Use a capital at the beginning.

Add a . at the end.

Look at That!

by B. G. Hennessy
illustrated by Seth Larson

I like to look at clouds.
Do you?

Look at all the clouds.
Look at the clouds play.

Look at that cloud!
Can you find a hat?
I see a hat on a cat.

Look at that cloud!

Can you find a man?

I see a man and a pan.

Look at that cloud!
Can you find a cub?
I see a cub in a tub.

Look at that cloud!

Can you find a bear?

I see a bear in a chair.

Look at all the clouds.
The clouds are big and fat.
Those clouds make rain.

I like to look at rain.

Do you?

Can You Find It?

by Sharon Fear

illustrated by Wendy Edelson

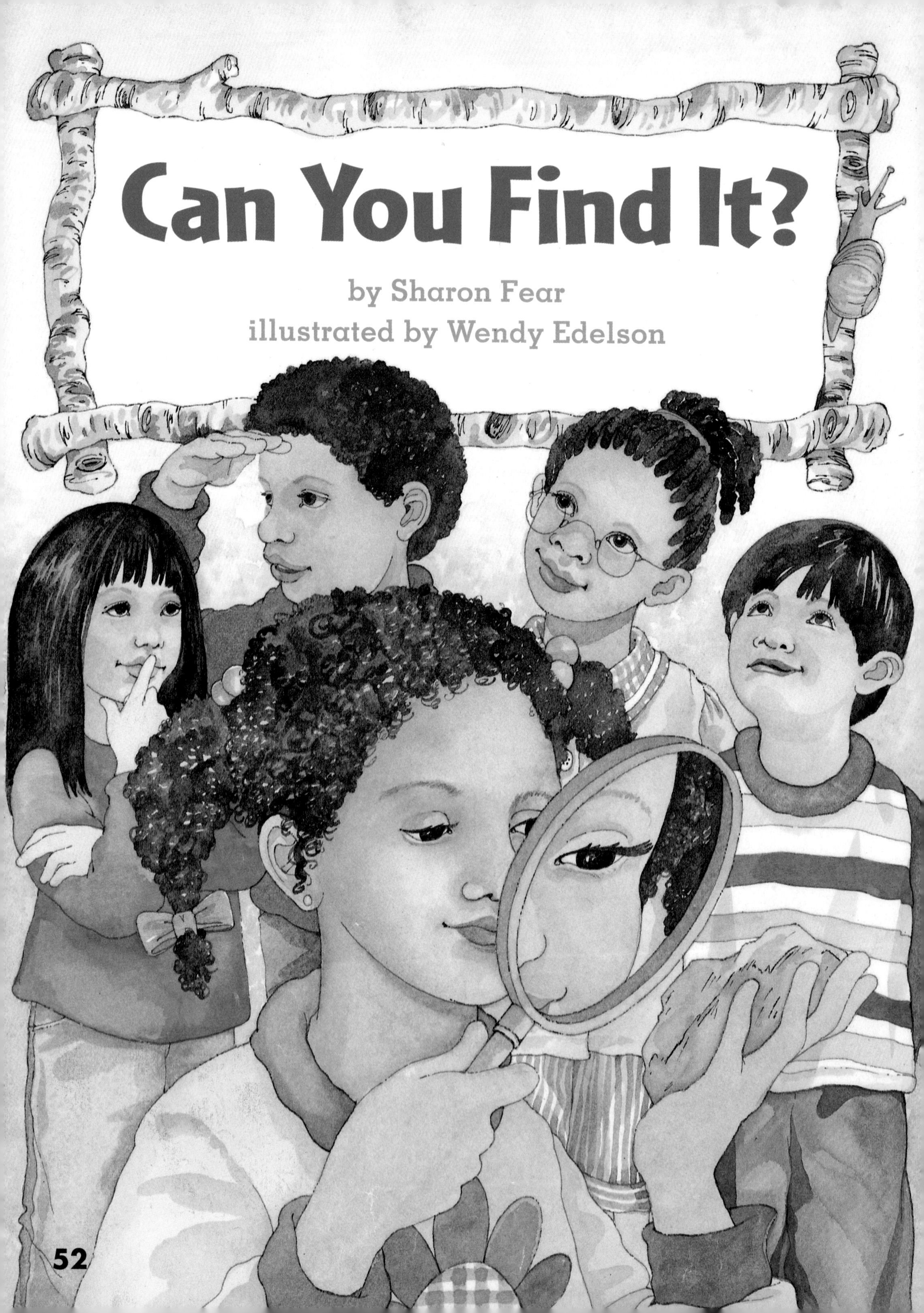

Make a snack.

Make a map.

Get a hat.

Get a bag.

Come with us.
Play with us.
We are all friends.

Find the snail!

Can Sam find a snail?

Not in a web.

A spider is in the web.

Can Pat find a snail?

Not in a nest.

A bird is in the nest.

Can Jan find a snail?

Not in a hole.

An ant is in the hole.

Can Nat find a snail?

Look at that!

A snail is on the leaf.

Come with us.

Play with us.

We are all friends.

Find the snail!

About the Author

Sharon Fear and her family lived on a farm. Later they moved to a ranch. Her neighbors liked to tell and retell stories. "Maybe that's where I learned to love stories so good that you could tell them again and again," says Ms. Fear.

Start

Read Together

Reader Response

Let's Talk

The children in the story look for a snail.
What animal would you like to look for?
Why?

Let's Think

The children in the story found a snail.
They left it alone.
Why was this a good idea?

Test Prep

Let's Write

Where did the children in the story look for snails?
Where would you look for animals?
Make a poster of an animal you might find.
Write a sentence about it.

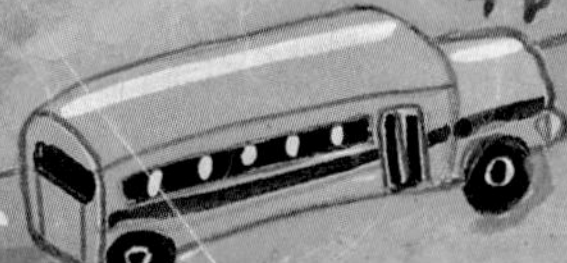

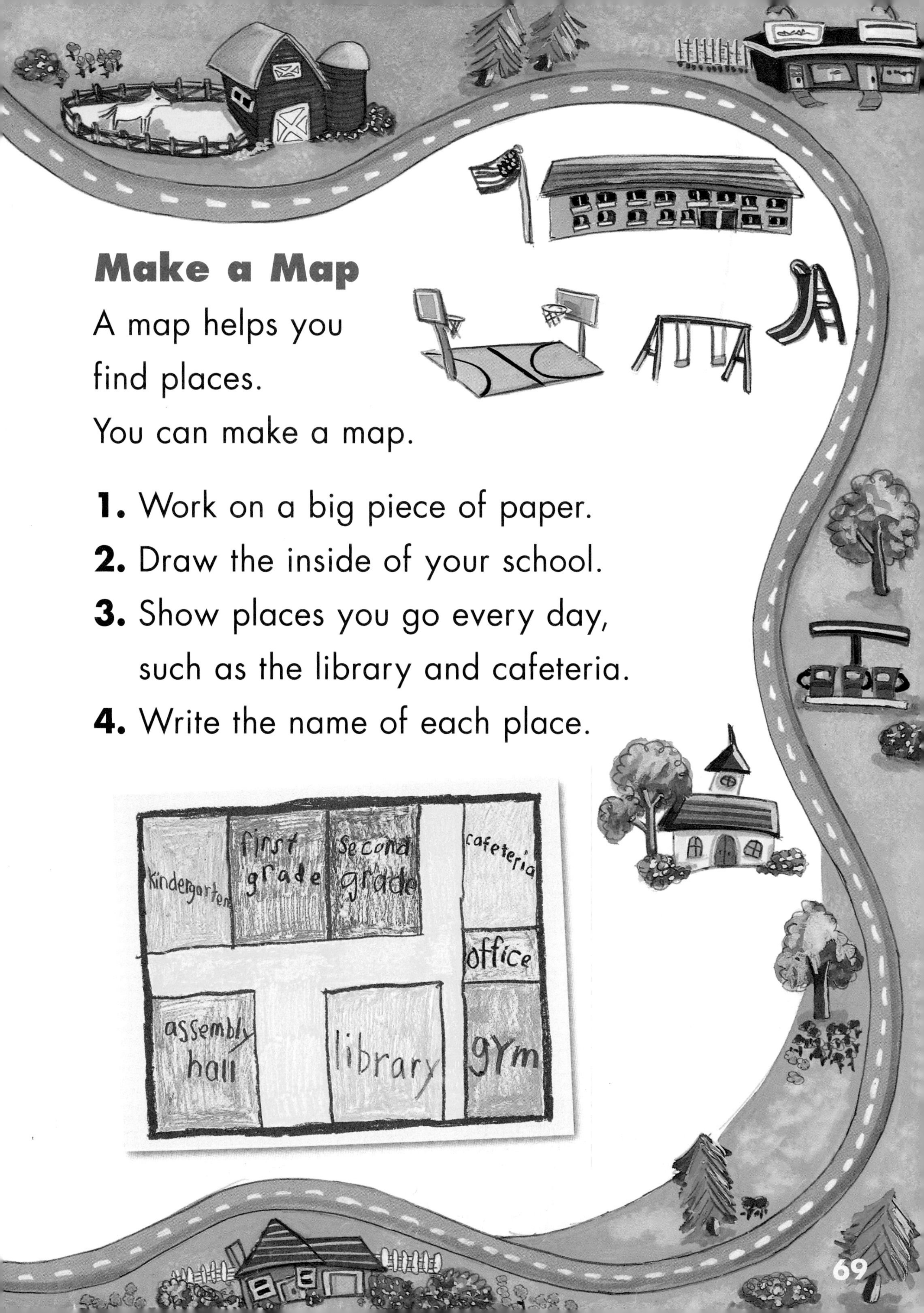

Make a Map

A map helps you find places. You can make a map.

1. Work on a big piece of paper.
2. Draw the inside of your school.
3. Show places you go every day, such as the library and cafeteria.
4. Write the name of each place.

Language Arts

Naming Parts

Every sentence has a naming part. The **naming part** names a person, animal, or thing.

The deer is hiding.
The girl is looking.

What **naming parts** are in the sentences?

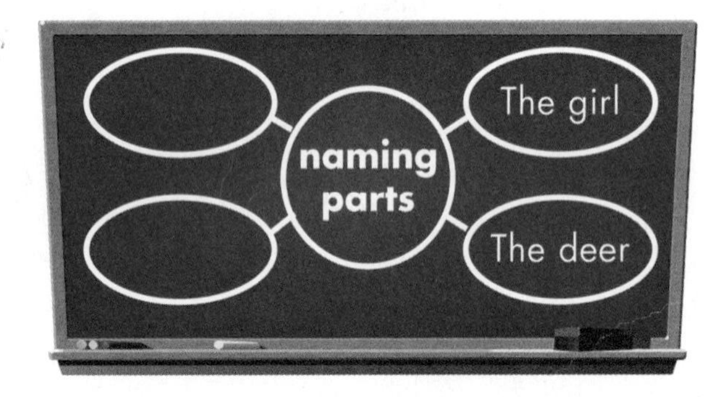

Talk

Look at the pictures.

Tell who or what is doing each thing.

Add naming parts to the web.

Write

Write the sentences.

Use naming parts from your web.

1. __ shines.

2. __ grows tall.

3. __ are flying.

Write your own sentences.

Make each tell a complete idea.

Circle the naming parts.

Phonics Story

What Did I See?

by Helen Lester

illustrated by Benton Mahan

I went to the park.

What did I see?

I saw a slide.

Slip!

I saw a ball.

Kick!

I saw a duck walk.

Quack!

I saw a big hill.

I win!

I saw a tree.

I hid!

I saw a rock. Oh, no.

Trip!

I saw kids.

Lucky me!

I Went Walking

by
Sue Williams

illustrated by
Julie Vivas

I went walking.

What did you see?

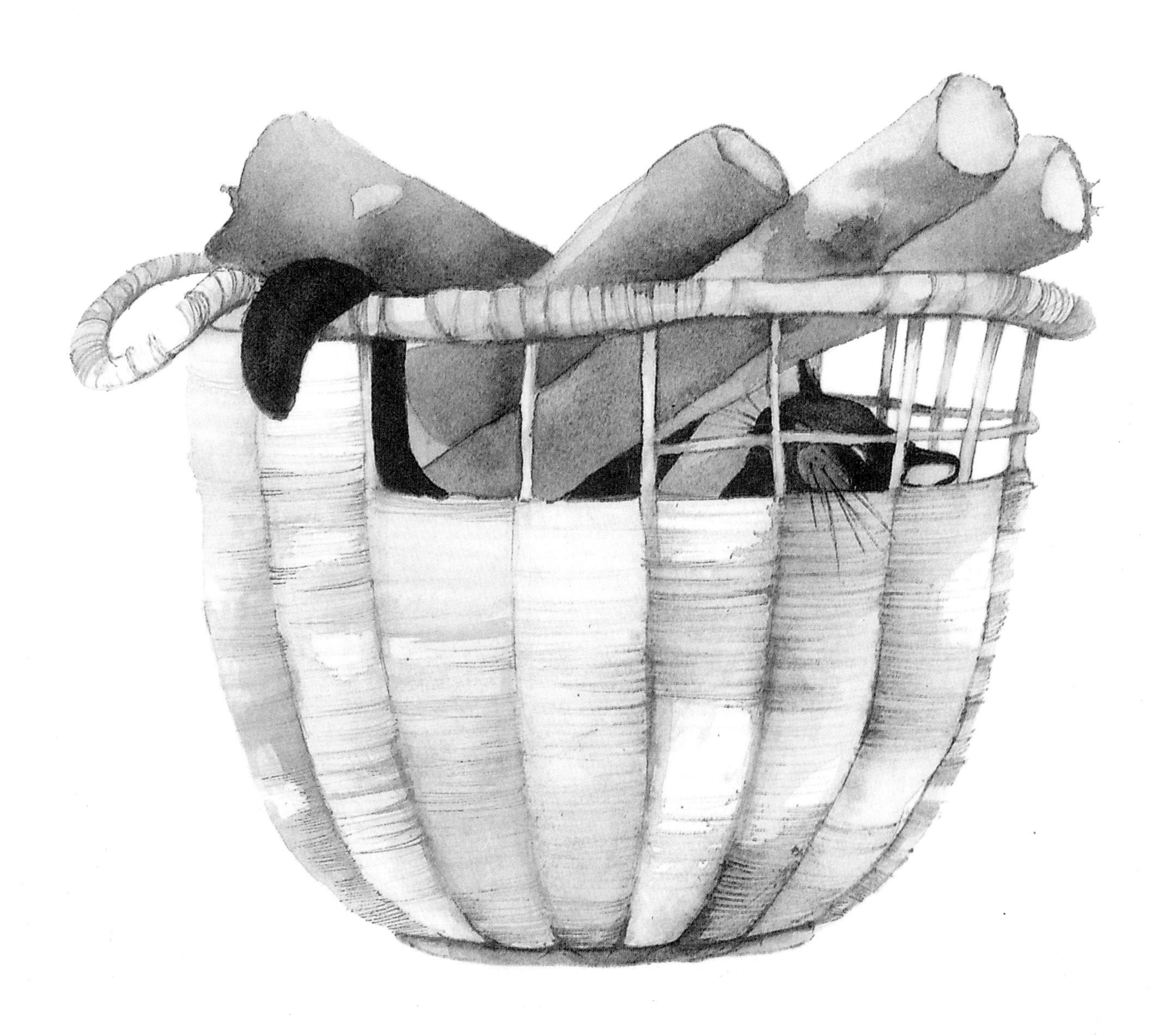

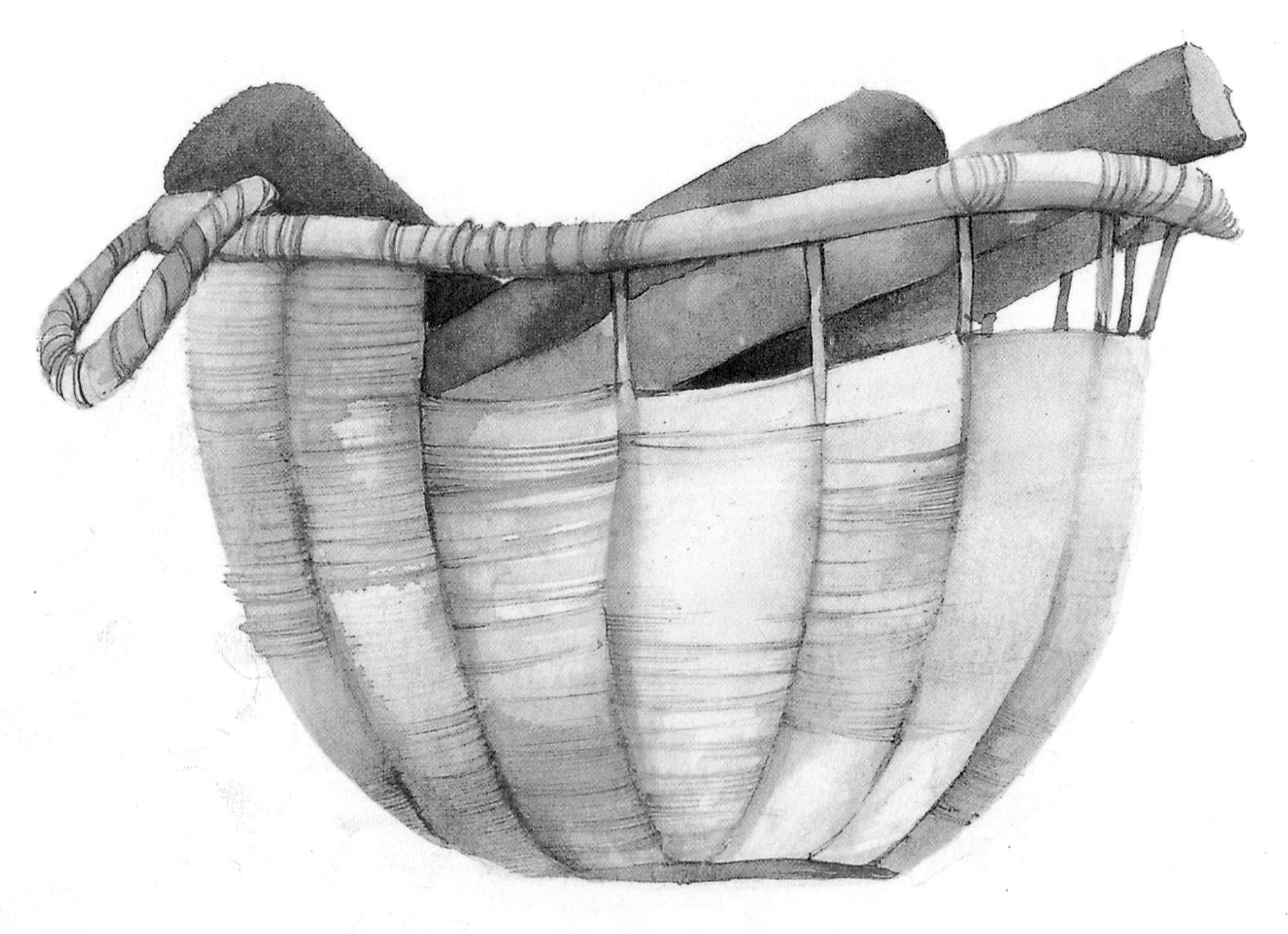

I saw a black cat
looking at me.

I went walking.

What did you see?

I saw a brown horse
looking at me.

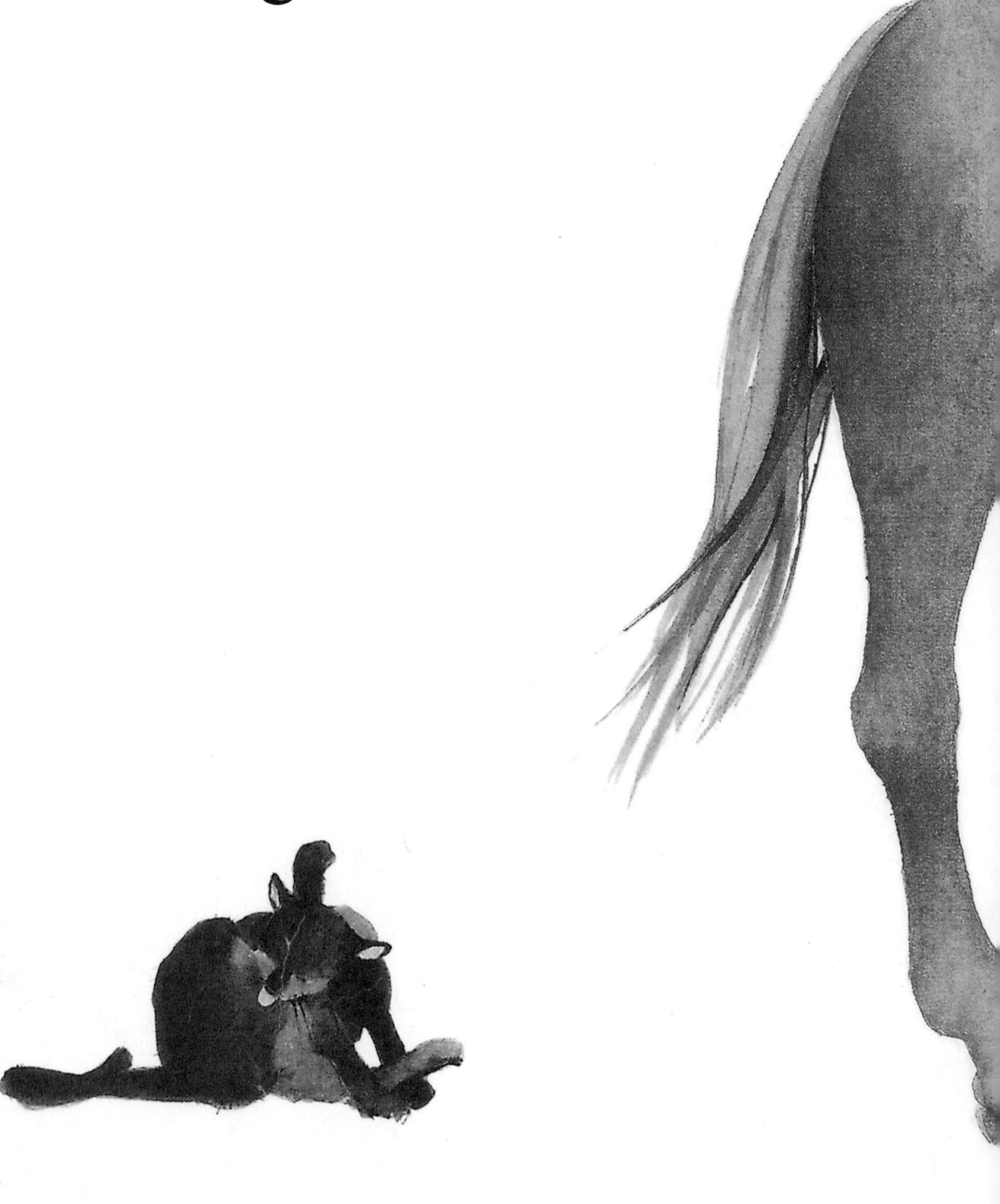

I went walking.

What did you see?

I saw a red cow
looking at me.

I went walking.

What did you see?

I saw a green duck
looking at me.

I went walking.

What did you see?

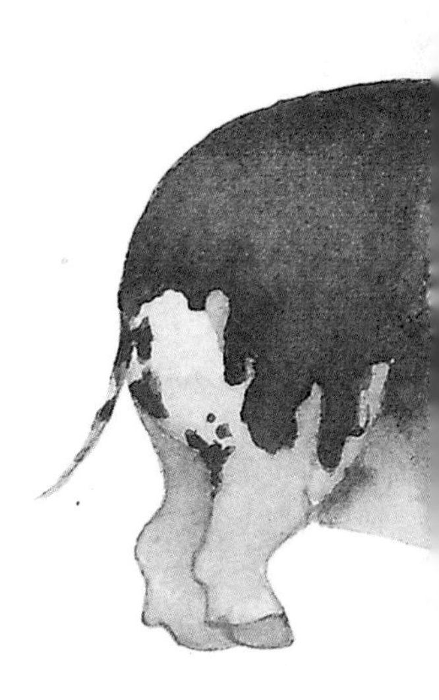

I saw a pink pig
looking at me.

I went walking.

What did you see?

I saw a yellow dog
looking at me.

I went walking.

What did you see?

I saw a lot of animals following me!

About the Author and the Illustrator

Sue Williams lives on a farm. She raises sheep and grows apples. *I Went Walking* is her first picture book. She wrote it for her nieces and nephews.

Julie Vivas begins her pictures with pencil. She finishes them with watercolor. She says, "I enjoy the wet paint melting into the wet paper."

Quack, Quack!

by Dr. Seuss

We have two ducks. One blue. One black.
And when our blue duck goes "Quack-quack"
our black duck quickly quack-quacks back.
The quacks Blue quacks make her quite a quacker
but Black is a quicker quacker-backer.

Read Together

Reader Response

Let's Talk

Which animals in the story have you seen? Where did you see them?

Let's Think

What colors are the animals in the story? What other colors could they be?

Test Prep

Let's Write

Pick the animal you like best from the story. Write a sentence to tell why you like it.

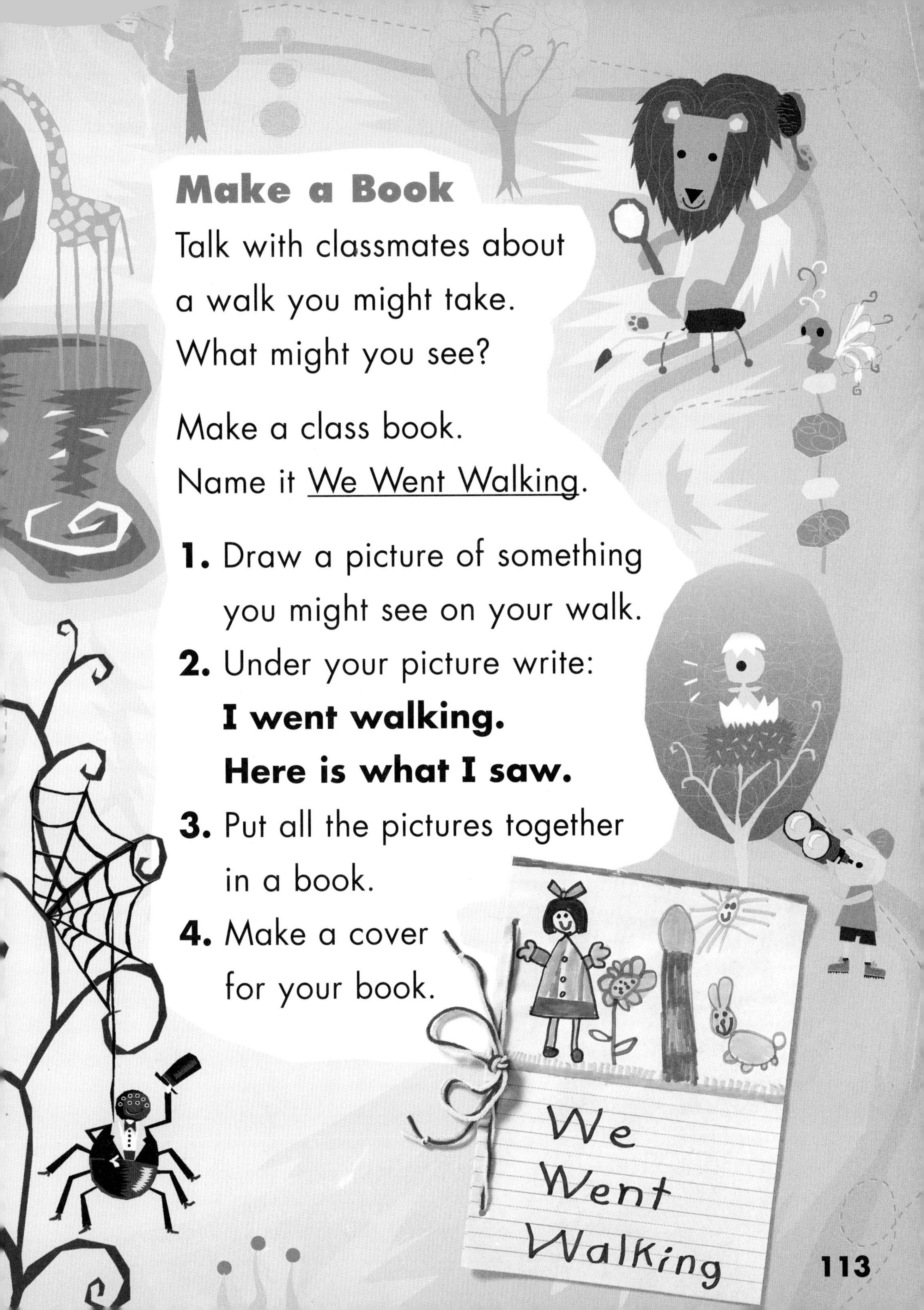

Make a Book

Talk with classmates about
a walk you might take.
What might you see?

Make a class book.
Name it We Went Walking.

1. Draw a picture of something you might see on your walk.
2. Under your picture write:
   I went walking.
   Here is what I saw.
3. Put all the pictures together in a book.
4. Make a cover for your book.

Read Together

Language Arts

Action Parts

Every sentence has two parts.
It has a naming part and an action part.
The **action part** tells what the person, animal, or thing does.

A boy **reads**. A girl **paints**.

What **action parts** are in the sentences?

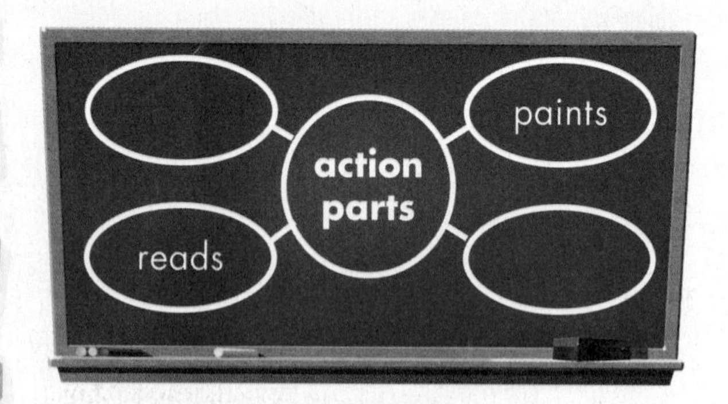

Talk

Look at the pictures.
Tell what someone or something does in the classroom.
Add action parts to the web.

Write

Write the sentences.
Use action parts from
your web.

1. The rabbit __.
2. The teacher __.
3. The boy __.

Write your own sentences.
Make each tell a complete idea.
Circle the action parts.

Fish Mix

by Judy Nayer

I see one fish.

I see two.

I see three fish.

Will they swim to you?

How many yellow fish?

How many blue?

I see a mix of fish.

How about you?

Six little fish.

They swim like this.

One big fish.

Its fins go swish!

A mix of fish!

Why do they stop?

I see why!

A man is on top!

How Many Fish?

by Caron Lee Cohen
illustrated by S. D. Schindler

How many fish?

How many fish?

Six little fish in the bay.

Where do they go?
Why do they go?

Six little fish on their way.

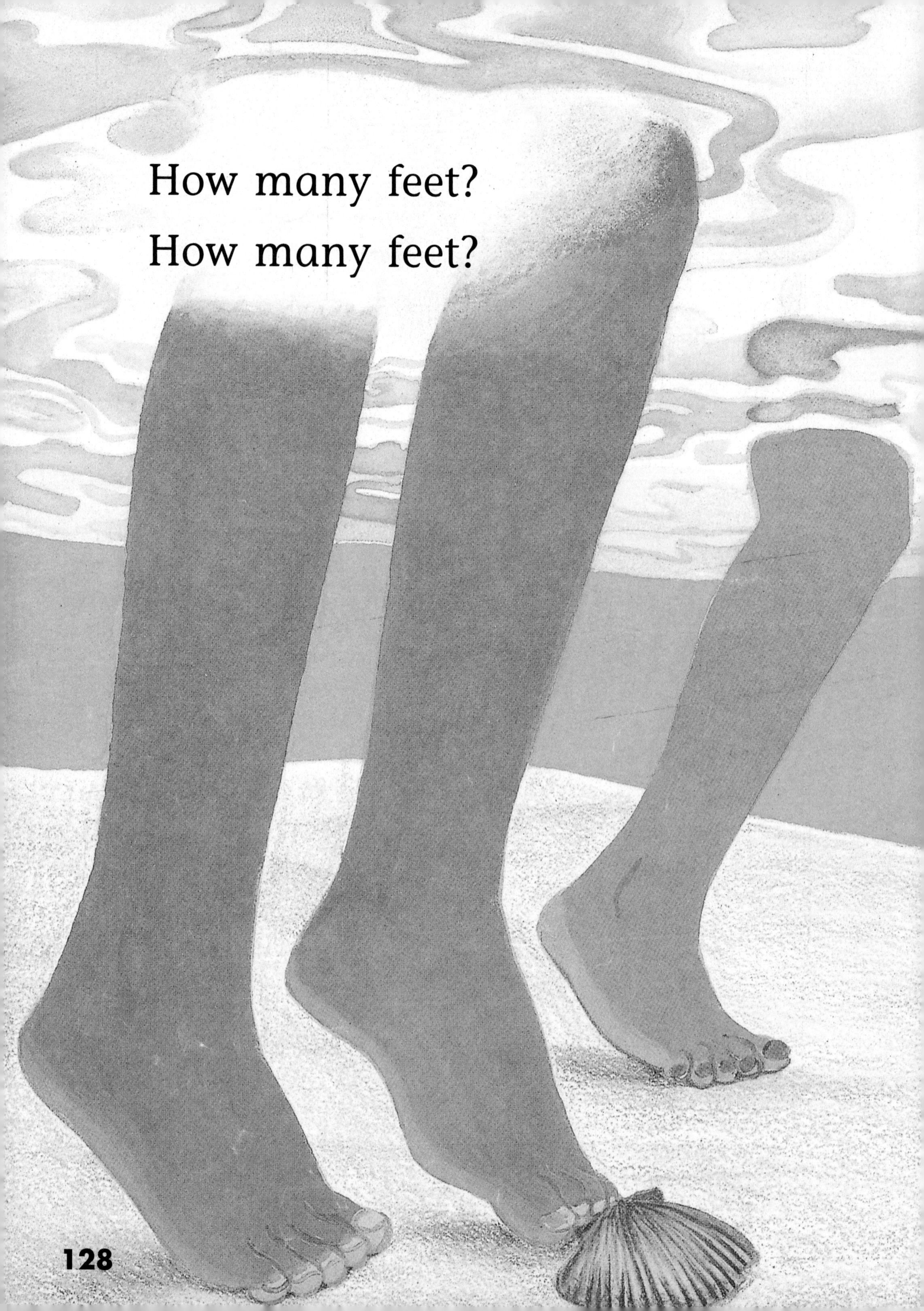

How many feet?
How many feet?

Six little feet in the bay.

Where do they go?
Why do they go?

Six little feet on their way.

How many fish?
How many fish?

One yellow fish in the bay.

Where's yellow fish?
Where's yellow fish?

Poor yellow fish lost its way.

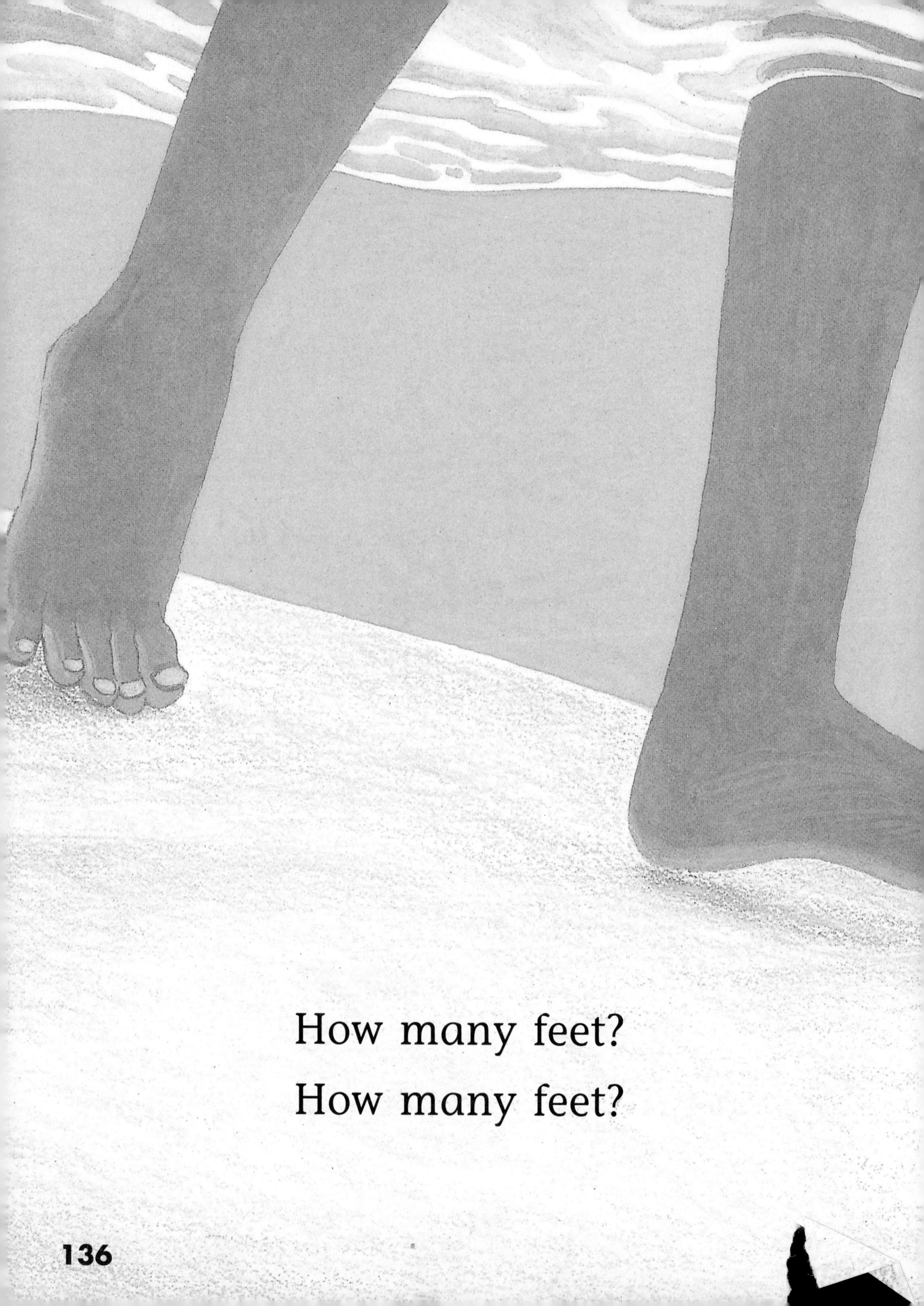

How many feet?
How many feet?

Two little feet in the bay.

Where's the red pail?
Where's the red pail?

Two little feet dash away.

One happy fish.
One happy fish.

One happy fish on its way!

How many fish?
How many fish?

Six little fish in the bay!

About the Author and the Illustrator

Caron Lee Cohen has always liked going to the beach. She likes to swim. She has seen many fish in the water!

S. D. Schindler was known for his drawings even as a child in school.

Mr. Schindler likes having fish around. He made two ponds near his house. They are filled with goldfish.

One, Two, Three, Four, Five

a Mother Goose rhyme

One, two, three, four, five,
Once I caught a fish alive,
Six, seven, eight, nine, ten,
Then I let it go again.
Why did you let it go?
Because it bit my finger so.
Which finger did it bite?
The little finger on the right.

Read Together

Reader Response

Let's Talk

The children in the story
like to play in the bay.
Where do you like to play?

Let's Think

Do you think the children knew
a fish was under their pail?
Why?

Test Prep

Let's Write

Look at the pictures in the story.
Write funny sentences about fish.

Make Number Sentences

You can use fish to make number sentences.

1. Work with a partner.
2. Cut out fish from colored paper.
   Also cut out +, -, and = signs.
3. Give your partner some fish
   and the +, -, and = signs.
4. Your partner makes a number
   sentence with the fish.
   Is it right?
5. Now it's your turn.

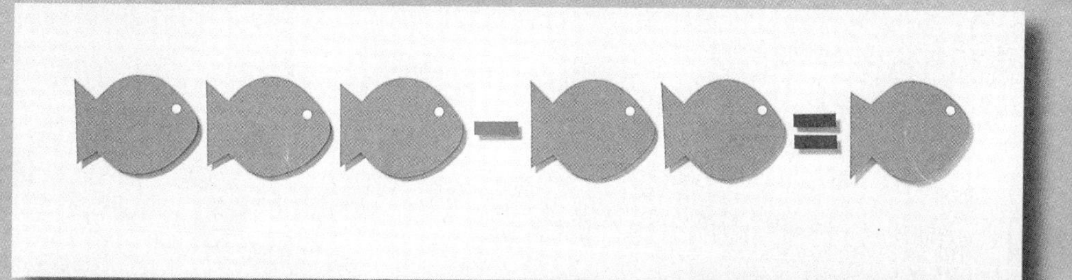

Read Together

Language Arts

Word Order

The order of words tells what a sentence means.
Which sentence tells about something in the picture?

A fish is under a pail.
A pail is under a fish.

Talk

Look at the picture.
Say a sentence about the picture.
Let a friend change the word order to make a different sentence.

Write

Look at the picture.

Read the pairs of sentences.

Write the sentence that tells what you see.

The octopus plays the piano.
The piano plays the octopus.

The fish is faster than the snail.
The snail is faster than the fish.

Write two sentences of your own about the picture.

Change the word order in each.

Let a friend tell you which tells about the picture.

JOG, FROG, JOG

by Barbara Gregorich
illustrated by Bernard Adnet

This is a frog.
The frog likes to jog.

He jogs in the day.

He jogs in the night.

Oh, oh! This is a dog.

The dog does not like frogs.

The dog sees the frog!

Jog, frog, jog!

Jog in the water!

Jog in the fog!

Go, frog, go!

Jog into the log!

The log stops the dog.

Jog, frog! Jog around that dog!

Poor dog!

Tadpole to Frog

by Fay Robinson

Here is some water.

Here are some eggs.

This is a tadpole.

Here come his legs!

His tail gets little.
His body gets plump.

Soon he's a frog.
Look at him jump!

Where does he go?
Into water, on logs.

We like to see tadpoles
turn into frogs!

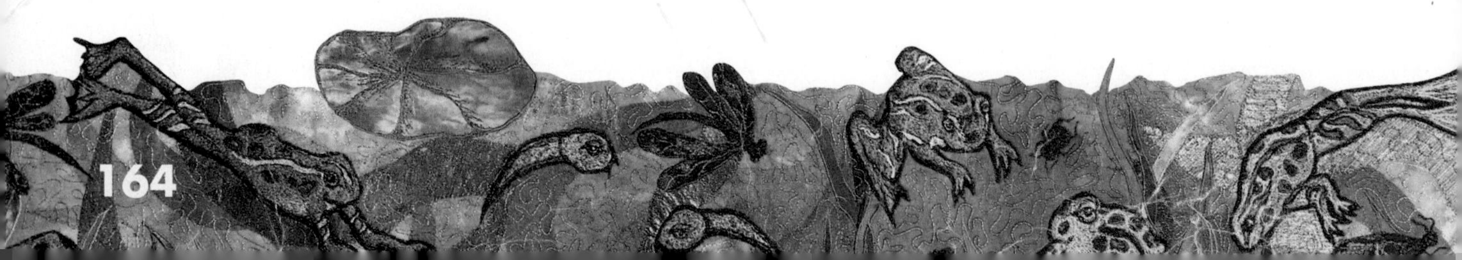

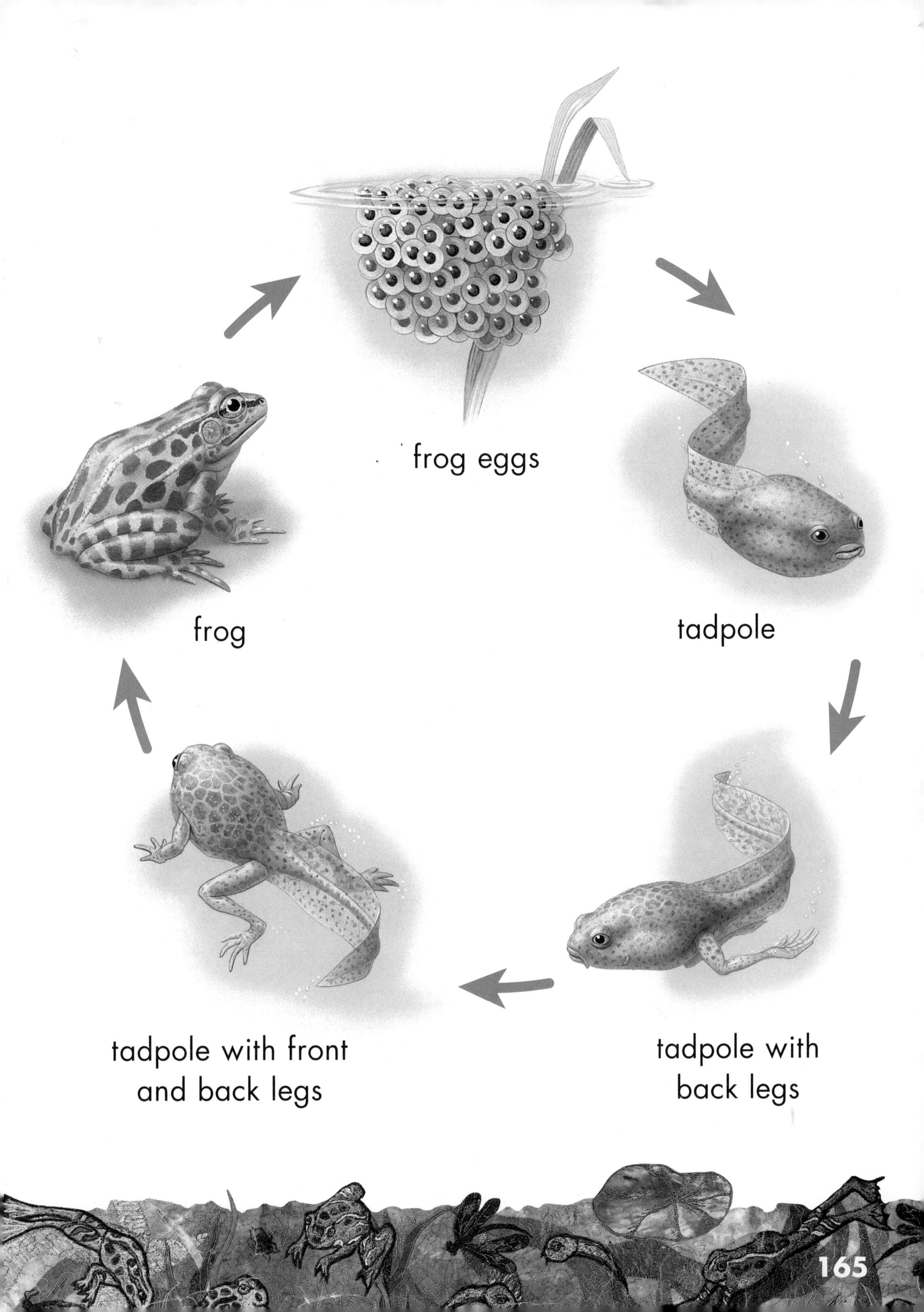
frog eggs
tadpole
tadpole with
back legs
tadpole with front
and back legs
frog

About the Author

Fay Robinson

Do you think spiders, snakes, beetles, lizards, and frogs are creepy? Fay Robinson doesn't. She loves writing about them. She thinks that they are fun to learn about.

Ms. Robinson was a teacher before she became a writer. She and her students raised tadpoles. Every morning her students would check to find out if the tadpoles had changed.

Notice

by David McCord

I have a dog,
I had a cat.
I've got a frog
Inside my hat.

Read Together

Reader Response

Let's Talk

Were you surprised by
the way the tadpole grew?
Why or why not?

Let's Think

Why do you think the
tadpole's tail becomes
shorter?

Test Prep

Let's Write

Pretend you are a tadpole.
Write about each stage of your life.
Look back at page 165 for help.

Make a Frog Poster

Show what you know about frogs and tadpoles.

1. Write a fact about a tadpole or frog.
2. Draw a picture to show that fact.
3. Hang your drawings and facts on the wall.

Read Together

Language Arts

Telling Sentences

A **telling sentence** tells something.

It begins with a capital letter.

It ends with a **.** .

The frog jumps**.**

This is a telling sentence.

It tells what the frog does.

Talk

Tell what you see in the picture.

Then make up a story about it.

One person starts with a telling sentence.

Others add sentences when it is their turn.

Write

Write the telling sentences correctly.

Begin with a capital letter.

End with a **.** .

1. the turtle sits on a log

2. fish swim in the water

3. some animals fly

Work with a partner.

Write a telling sentence about a water animal.

Use a capital letter and a **.** .

Phonics Story

A Big Job

by Kana Riley

illustrated by Stacey Schuett

The sun is hot.

Birds sing.

Mom is singing too.

She digs and digs.

She does not stop.

Beans go in the dirt.

Mom is watering the beans.

Look at them go.

They do not stop.

Mom gets a pot.
She picks the beans one
by one.

Mom is filling the
pot to the top.
It is a big job.

Mom is licking her lips.

I am too.

It is time to eat.
We eat the beans one
by one.

Sweet Potato Pie

by Anne Rockwell
illustrated by Carolyn Croll

Pa picks sweet potatoes
one by one.

Why, oh, why?

Sweet potato pie!

Grandma bakes them
till they're done.

Why, oh, why?
Sweet potato pie!

Gramps stops chopping.

Ma stops washing.

Tom stops swimming.
Why, oh, why?

Sis stops
swinging.

Bob starts
singing.

Come and get my
sweet potato pie!

Everybody coming
one by one.

Why, oh, why?
Sweet potato pie!

Everybody eating
till there's none.

My, oh, my.
Sweet potato pie!

About the Author

Anne Rockwell

As a child, Anne Rockwell often visited her grandparents. They lived on a farm in Mississippi. They grew their own food as the family in *Sweet Potato Pie* did.

Ms. Rockwell remembers her grandmother telling stories in the kitchen. Her grandmother read to her too. She taught Ms. Rockwell to love reading.

Read Together

Reader Response

Let's Talk

The people in the story like the smell of sweet potato pie. What food smells good to you?

Let's Think

Is sweet potato pie one of the family's favorite foods? How do you know?

Test Prep

Let's Write

The family in the story likes sweet potatoes. Think of a food your family likes to eat. Write about it.

Make A Song

Sweet Potato Pie is almost like a song.
It is fun to read out loud.
Try this.

1. Divide into three groups.
2. Group 1 reads the parts about the family.
3. Group 2 reads these lines: **Why, oh, why? Sweet potato pie!**
4. Group 3 plays instruments to add the beat.
5. Practice until it sounds just right.

Read Together

Language Arts

Asking Sentences

A **question** asks something.

A question is an asking sentence.

It begins with a capital letter.

It ends with a **?** .

Who made the pizza**?**

This is a question.

It asks something.

Talk

Look at the pictures.

Work with a partner.

Ask a question about a picture.

Your partner answers the question with a telling sentence.

Write

Write the questions correctly.
Begin with a capital letter.
End with a **?** .

1. is the boy's name Jack
2. are the cookies still warm
3. who wants some pizza

Write a question of your own.
Use a capital and a **?** .
Then write the answer.

Vocabulary Review

Words I Know

The Nap

Oh, Cats!

away no
come will
down

What Did I See?

I Went Walking

did walk
me went
saw

Look at That!

Can You Find It?

all make
are play
find

Fish Mix

How Many Fish?

happy on
how they
many why

Jog, Frog, Jog

Tadpole to Frog

does this
he water
into

A Big Job

Sweet Potato Pie

by stop
eat them
sing

Read Together

Test Talk

Taking a Test

A test has questions for you to answer.
You answer a question by marking
the right answer.
Only one answer will be right.

Here is a question about *Can You Find It?*

1. What animal did the children look for in the story?

(A) a frog

(B) a bear

(C) a snail

Use a pencil. Mark only one answer.
Fill in the bubble next to , , or .
Stay inside the lines.

Here is how one boy marked his answer.

Try it!

Read the questions.

Tell which question has the answer filled in right.

Tell why.

2. What did the children see in a nest?

- **(A) a bird**
- **(B) a spider**
- **(C) a snail**

3. Where did the children find a snail?

- **(A) in a nest**
- **(B) in a hole**
- **(C) on a leaf**

Pictionary
Animals

Pets

Farm Animals

Bird

Insect

Wild Animals

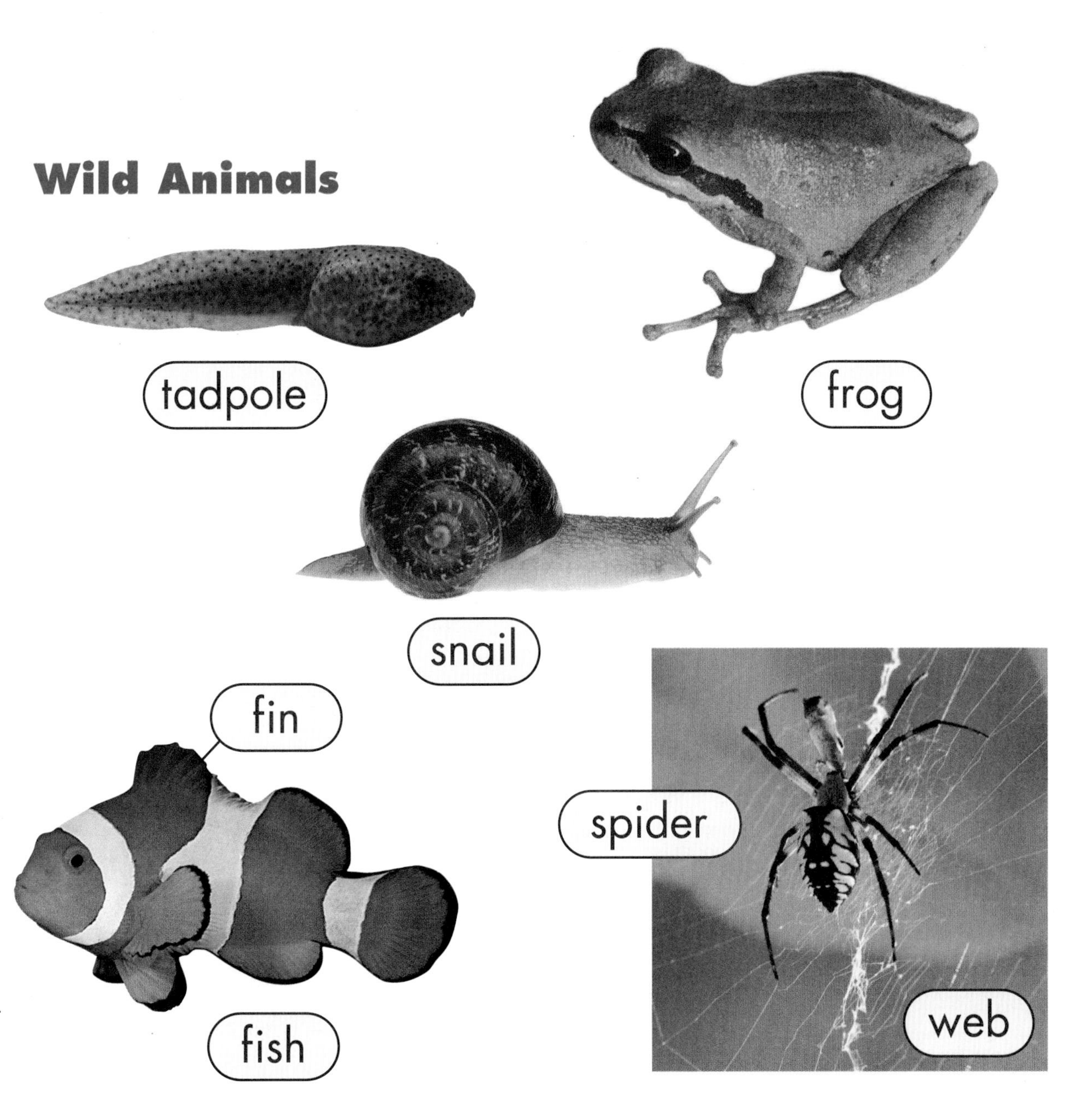

Tested Word List

The Nap
Oh, Cats!

away
come
down
no
will

What Did I See?
I Went Walking

did
me
saw
walk
went

Jog, Frog, Jog
Tadpole to Frog

does
he
into
this
water

Look at That!
Can You Find It?

all
are
find
make
play

Fish Mix
How Many Fish?

happy
how
many
on
they
why

A Big Job
Sweet Potato Pie

by
eat
sing
stop
them

Acknowledgments

Text

Page 18: *Oh, Cats!* by Nola Buck, pictures by Nadine Bernard Westcott, pp. 4–24. Text copyright © 1997 by Nola Buck. Illustrations copyright © 1997 by Nadine Bernard Westcott, Inc. Reprinted by permission of HarperCollins Publishers, Inc.
Page 80: *I Went Walking* by Sue Williams, illustrated by Julie Vivas. Text copyright © 1989 by Sue Williams, illustrations copyright © by Julie Vivas, reprinted by permission of Harcourt, Inc.
Page 111: "Quack, Quack!" from *Oh, Say Can You Say?* by Dr. Seuss, TM and copyright © by Dr. Seuss Enterprises, L.P., 1979. Used by permission of Random House, Inc.
Page 124: *How Many Fish?* by Caron Lee Cohen, pictures by S. D. Schindler, pp. 6–25. Text copyright © 1998 by Caron Lee Cohen. Illustrations copyright © 1998 by S. D. Schindler. Reprinted by permission of HarperCollins Publishers, Inc.
Page 150: *Jog, Frog, Jog* by Barbara Gregorich, pp. 2, 4, 6, 8, 10, 12, 14, 16, 18, 20, 22, 24, 26, 28, & 30. Copyright School Zone Publishing Inc., 1984.
Page 167: "Notice" from *One at a Time* by David McCord. Copyright 1952 by David McCord. Reprinted by permission of Little, Brown and Company.
Page 180: *Sweet Potato Pie* by Anne Rockwell, pp. 5, 7–9, 11, 13, 15, 17–18, 20, 23, 25, 27–28, 30, & 32. Text copyright © 1996 by Anne Rockwell. Reprinted by permission of Random House, Inc.

Artists

Maryjane Begin, cover, 8–9
Jackie Urbanovic, 10–17
Nadine Bernard Westcott, 18–39
Clive Scruton, 40–43
Seth Larson, 44–51
Wendy Edelson, 52–67
Ilene Richard, 68–71
Benton Mahan, 72–79
Julie Vivas, 80–110
Eileen Mueller-Neill, 111
Stacy Peterson, 112–115
S. D. Schindler, 124–143
Kathy Lengyel, 145
Franklin Hammond, 146–149
Bernard Adnet, 150–157
Ellen Eddy, (border) 158
Walter Stuart, 165
Kathy McCord, 167
Pamela Paulsrud, (calligraphy) 167
Bobbi Tull, 168–171
Stacey Schuett, 172–179
Carolyn Croll, 180–203

Photographs

Every effort has been made to secure permission and provide appropriate credit for photographic material. The publisher deeply regrets any omission and pledges to correct errors called to their attention in subsequent editions.

Unless otherwise acknowledged, all photographs are the property of Scott Foresman, a division of Pearson Education. Page abbreviations are as follows: (t) top, (b) bottom, (l) left, (r) right, (ins) inset, (s) spot, (bk) background.

Page 39 (T) Courtesy HarperCollins Publishers
Page 110 (TL) Courtesy Harcourt Brace & Company, Photo: Doug Nicholas; (TR) Courtesy Harcourt Brace & Company
Pages 116,117,118 (TL, BCL, BCR, BL, BR) Norbert Wu
Page 118 (TR) Steven David Miller/Animals Animals/Earth Scenes; (TCL) Andrew G. Wood/Photo Researchers; (TCR) Carl Roessler/Tony Stone Images
Page 119 (TL, TR) Norbert Wu; (TCL, TCR) Superstock, Inc.; (BCL) Fred Bavendam/Minden Pictures; (BCR) M. Gibbs/OSF/Animals Animals/Earth Scenes; (BL, BR) Norbert Wu
Page 120 M. Gibbs/OSF/Animals Animals/Earth Scenes
Page 121 James D. Watt/Mo Yung Productions/Norbert Wu
Pages 122–123 Norbert Wu
Page 144 (TL) Courtesy Caron Lee Cohen, Photo: Elaine B. Cohen; (C) Kip Simons for Scott Foresman
Page 158 Nathan Cohen/Visuals Unlimited
Page 159 Harry Rogers/NAS/Photo Researchers
Page 160 John Mitchell/Photo Researchers
Page 161 Harry Rogers/NAS/Photo Researchers
Pages 162–163 (T) Stephen Dalton/Photo Researchers
Page 163 (B) Rod Planck/TOM STACK & ASSOCIATES
Page 164 Stephen Dalton/Photo Researchers
Page 166 (CR, CL, BR, TR) PhotoDisc, Inc.; (TC) Ron Davis for Scott Foresman
Page 197 Courtesy Anne Rockwell
Page 206 cat, dog, pig, horse, cow, duck, PhotoDisc, Inc.; ant, Artville
Page 207 tadpole, Harry Rogers/NAS/Photo Researchers; frog, spider/web, bear/cub, PhotoDisc, Inc.; snail, Artville